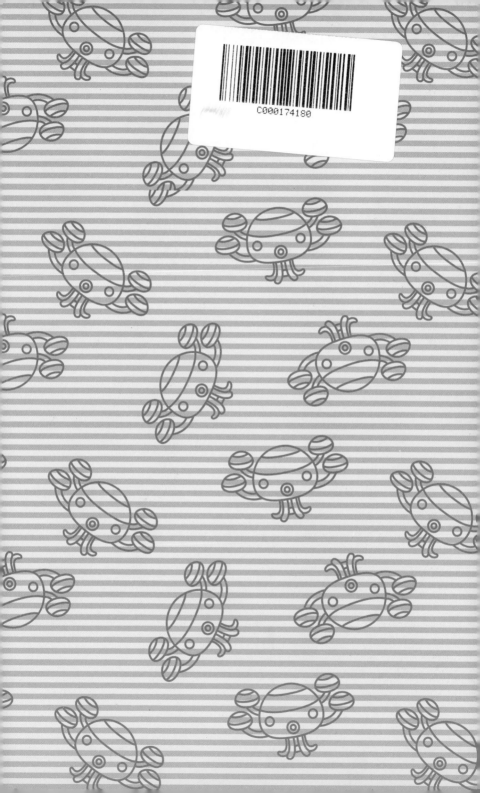

THIS OCTONAUTS HOLIDAY ANNUAL BELONGS TO

_____

OCTONAUTS

HOLIDAY ANNUAL

CONTENTS

EXPLORE . RESCUE . PROTECT

EGMONT
We bring stories to life

First published in Great Britain in 2012 by Egmont UK Limited, 239 Kensington High Street, London W8 6SA

Written by Jane Riordan and Leah James. Designed by Andrea Pollock.
OCTONAUTS™ OCTOPOD™ Copyright © 2012 Chorion Rights Limited. All rights reserved.

ISBN 978 1 4052 6182 1
51261/1
Printed in China

BARNACLES

CAPTAIN

HIS MISSION: To lead the Octonauts as they explore, rescue and protect!

BIG FACT: He is a mighty weightlifter and the strongest of the Octonauts.

CATCHPHRASE: Octonauts, let's do this!

DID YOU KNOW? He plays the accordion.

KWAZII

LIEUTENANT

HIS MISSION: To bravely swashbuckle his way through undersea adventures.

BIG FACT: His favourite ship is the Gup-B – the fastest sub in the fleet.

CATCHPHRASE: Shiver me whiskers!

DID YOU KNOW? There is actually nothing wrong with the eye under his patch!

PESO

MEDIC

HIS MISSION: To help any creature who is hurt or sick, no matter what!

BIG FACT: Peso's sick bay has a large tank for any hurt sea creatures.

CATCHPHRASE: Flappity flippers!

DID YOU KNOW? Peso is the youngest member of the crew.

TWEAK

ENGINEER

HER MISSION: To keep the Octopod and the Gups running smoothly.

BIG FACT: It was Tweak who designed all of the Gups.

CATCHPHRASE: You got it, Cap!

DID YOU KNOW? She sometimes keeps carrots in her toolbox and tools in her lunchbox!

SHELLINGTON

FIELD RESEARCHER

HIS MISSION: To look at life through his magnifying glass – taking in every detail.

BIG FACT: He's the only Octonaut who can understand what the Vegimals are saying.

CATCHPHRASE: Jumpin' jellyfish!

DID YOU KNOW? He loves clam ice cream!

DASHI

OFFICIAL PHOTOGRAPHER

HIS MISSION: To photograph research and rescue missions.

BIG FACT: Dashi is also the ship navigator and computer expert.

CATCHPHRASE: Say seaweed!

DID YOU KNOW? Her favourite colour is pink!

INKLING

PROFESSOR

HIS MISSION: He founded the Octon... advance underwater research and p...

BIG FACT: He spends most of his time... library but when he does go furth... sometimes travels in his blue h...

CATCHPHRASE: Fascinating!

DID YOU KNOW? He can read 8 books at once!

GUP-A IN ACTION!

Captain Barnacles drives the GUP-A, and up to five Octonauts can fit in. There's even a computer inside! This ship is well equipped and ready to cope with any tricky situation, in any of the undersea zones! Just like the time when a sea turtle got caught in a fast-moving current. It was the GUP-A that came to its rescue.

Find a sticker of a turtle and a torpedo ray to finish the scene.

OCTOFACT:

The propeller on this Gup can be replaced with a turbo option when extra speed is needed.

17

In the launch bay, Tweak was mending the GUP-B.

"Right, all fixed, again!" said Tweak. "And, I've added a turbo button so you can go extra fast in an emergency."

"Aye," said Kwazii. He jumped into the GUP-B. "I'm going to test-drive her now. Open the Octohatch, me hearty!"

"Remember, Kwazii," Tweak called. "The turbo button will make you go **VERY** fast. Only use it in an emergency!"

Meanwhile, in the control room, Dashi was watching the weather screen.

"Cap!" she cried. "There's a big storm coming!"

Captain Barnacles looked through the Octoscope at the sea. The water was swirling around. He was very worried.

"The storm is heading straight for us! Dashi, sound the Octoalert!"

ADD YOUR
OCTOALERT
STICKER
HERE!

OCTOFACT:

Thunderstorms create very strong winds and heavy rain.

OCTONAUTS TO THE HQ

Once everyone had arrived in the control room, Captain Barnacles gave the Octonauts important orders.

"Dashi, tell us when the storm comes closer!"

"Peso, close the outer portals!"

"Tweak, pull in the Octopod arms!"

"Kwazii, turn off the engines— Kwazii?" Captain Barnacles looked around the room. "Where is he?"

"Oh no," said Tweak. "Kwazii's still outside, test-driving the GUP-B!"

KWAZII? WHERE IS HE?

In the GUP-B, Kwazii had just pressed the turbo button. "Yeow!" he cried as the Gup sped forwards, powered by the turbo boost as well as the strong undersea current.

The strong current had also knocked over a baby lobster. Kwazii drove back to help him.

The baby lobster shook Kwazii's paw to say thank you.

"Yeow! You have a strong grip for a little lobster!" said Kwazii.

The baby lobster giggled and scuttled off to join his big family.

WHOOSH!

Back in the control room, Captain Barnacles called Kwazii on the radio.

"Kwazii, there's a big storm only ten minutes away. You have to come back to the Octopod before it gets here!"

"Aye, sir!" said Kwazii. "Just let me do a quick check of the reef to make sure all the creatures are safe."

Kwazii zoomed around the reef, helping creatures to safety.

A couple of minutes later, Dashi radioed Kwazii: "You have six minutes left!"

"Aye aye," replied Kwazii. "I'm heading home now!"

Kwazii pressed the red turbo button. **WHOOSH!** The Gup shot off towards the Octopod.

But suddenly, the Gup was caught in a strong current. **CRASH!** Kwazii was trapped upside-down in the GUP-B! And the big storm was only five minutes away!

23

On board the Octopod, the crew had seen Kwazii's accident on the screen. Captain Barnacles jumped into the GUP-C and raced off to help his friend.

When he arrived, Barnacles hooked the GUP-C's tow line to the GUP-B. He tried to pull the GUP-B along, but suddenly, **_RRRRIP!_** The tow line snapped in half!

Kwazii and Barnacles were stuck, with only three minutes left before the big storm arrived!

OCTO-FACT:
Reef lobsters live on the ocean floor and crawl around rocky reefs.

Just then, the lobster family Kwazii had helped earlier swam up. They joined claws, and held the ends of the tow rope together. Captain Barnacles started up the GUP-C, and pulled along the GUP-B. The lobsters held on tightly.

Meanwhile, the storm was nearly at the Octopod. Dashi counted down: "Ten, nine, eight, seven, six, five, four, three ..."

Just in time, the rescue mission made it safely through the Octohatch.

"Yowzers!" said Kwazii. "We never would have made it without the strong lobster tow line!"

Everyone cheered, hooray! Except for Tweak. Now she had to fix the GUP-B, *again*!

YOWZERS!

KWAZII AND GUP-B

Can you spot three differences between the two pictures of Kwazii?

A

B

How many times does GUP-B appear in this wordsearch?

U	G	U	P	B
G	U	P	B	G
U	P	B	G	U
G	B	P	U	P
P	G	U	P	B

Write your answer here:

OCTOFACT:
The GUP-B has
an ejector seat!

26

Answers on page 58.

Can you guide Kwazii through the storm to the Octopod? Pick up the sea creatures along the way. Can you name them all?

FLYING FISH

SPECIAL FEATURES: Flying fish have special side fins that let them fly above the ocean!

HABITAT: Can be found in every ocean.

DIET: Plankton.

CHALLENGE: Colour in your own flying fish. They can have very colourful wings!

OCTOFACT:

Flying fish can travel as fast as a car, at over 43 miles per hour!

28

 GUP-B IN ACTION!

There is no doubt that there is only one Gup which can be called upon when flying through the air is needed! It's the GUP-B. With its flying mode it's the only sub able to catch up with a school of flying fish.

Find a sticker of the flying fish to finish the scene.

OCTOFACT:

This sub has an ejector seat plus a turbo button. It's no wonder it's Kwazii's favourite sub!

29

Following the letters clockwise, which four words can you find in this wheel?

Answers on page 58.

Practice writing some watery words!

sea water
current

The GUP-E has broken down in the sunlight zone! The Octonauts have come to tow it back to the Octopod.

Can you find which line leads to the Octopod? Make sure you don't pick up the whitetip shark or the sailfish!

WELL DONE!

Add a starfish sticker when you've found the answer!

31

Undersea dangers are all around you! The Octonauts are always on the lookout for trouble as they dive into action.

Put a danger alert sticker next to the things that could put the Octonauts at risk.

GIANT CLAM

CUTTLEFISH

UNDERWATER VOLCANO

ELECTRIC TORPEDO RAY

WHIRLPOOL

JELLYFISH

Answers on page 58.

SWASHBUCKLING COLOURING

Use the dots to help you colour in this picture of Kwazii.

Match these Midnight Zone creatures to their shadows.

A

B

C

1

2

3

OCTOFACT:

The Midnight Zone is the deepest part of the ocean.

34

Answers on page 58

GUP-C IN ACTION!

When Kwazii's Gup breaks down in a storm this tug-sub is called to action. With it's super towing power it is soon able to rescue the pirate in trouble!

Find a sticker of the GUP-B to finish the scene.

OCTOFACT:

When needed, this Gup can be fitted with an ice breaker.

35

LAB SPOTTING

Can you spot five differences between the two pictures of Shellington's laboratory?

36

How many test tubes can you count in picture B? Give yourself an Octoalert sticker when you've found the answer.

Answers on page 58.

PLAY BREAK

Kwazii and Dashi are taking a well-earned break to play in the Game Pod. Can you find stickers of them to add to the scene? The vegimals might like to join in too. You could also add stickers of green fish swimming past the window.

OCTOFACT:

The Game Pod is connected to the Launch Bay by a chute so if there is an emergency the Octonauts can be ready to explore, rescue and protect!

DANGER ALERT!

14

PICTURE SUMS

Peso has lots of patients in his Infirmary! Help him count the snot sea cucumbers, mushroom corals and starfish. Draw over the numbers when you know the answers.

and makes 5

and makes 6

and makes 7

40

GUP-D IN ACTION!

The Octopod sees a lot of action so it's no wonder that sometimes things break and need mending. And when they do, Tweak and the multi-purpose GUP-D set to work without delay!

OCTOFACT:

The pincers of this Gup can be changed into drills.

Find a sticker of Tweak to finish the scene.

41

SHIVER ME WHISKERS

Which of these objects would you expect a pirate like Kwazii to own? Draw a circle around them.

42

Answers on page 59.

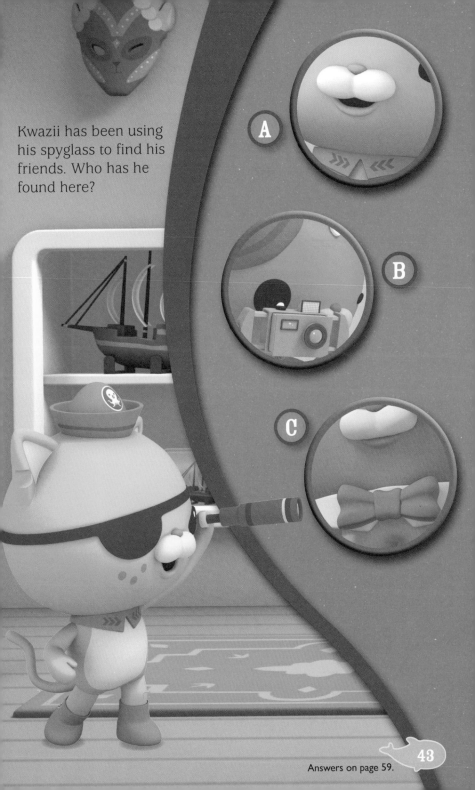

Kwazii has been using his spyglass to find his friends. Who has he found here?

A

B

C

Answers on page 59.

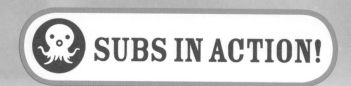

SUBS IN ACTION!

Five subs are out on a mission. It's your job to find them. Can you name them as well? Add an Octoalert sticker each time you find a sub.

DANGER ALERT!

DANGER ALERT!

44

FREEZING FUN!

The Octopod is trapped in Arctic ice!
Help Captain Barnacles navigate his way
out of the icy maze to the friendly narwhal.

When you've found the way out,
reward yourself with an
Octoalert sticker.

ADD YOUR
OCTOALERT
STICKER
HERE!

Answers on page 59.

THE ALBINO HUMPBACK WHALE

PESO	KWAZII	BARNACLES
SHELLINGTON	HUMPBACK WHALE	MUSHROOM CORAL

It was the middle of the night on the Octopod.

 couldn't sleep. He could hear strange noises.

There was something and WHITE and LOUD outside!

 was sure it was a Ghost Whale! "Sound the

Octoalert!" said  .

ADD YOUR
OCTOALERT
STICKER
HERE!

"Whatever it is, it may need our help," said and

the GUP-A was launched into the dark water to look for

the creature. soon spotted a strange pink-coloured

reef. "Octonauts, let's investigate!" said .

But there was something very strange about the reef.

"Jump!" said as the reef started to move.

"It's the Ghost Whale," whispered .

"I'm not a ghost!" said the creature, "I'm a white .

I'm a little pink though because I got sunburned!"

The whale had got sunburned going up to the surface to get

air.  knew that they'd have to find a lot of suncream

to help this huge  . Just then had a brilliant

idea. He remembered that in his pirate days, when he was

once stranded on a desert island, he had used

as suncream.

But the nearest  was a long way away. The

 was too sore to swim that far and so

called for some Gup backup. "I need all of them!"

he said. Together the Gups helped the through

the water, while explained that their new

friend was a very rare albino  .

"Ahoy, straight ahead!" called .

All the Octonauts set to work rubbing the oozy

over the 's sunburned back. "I never knew there

was such a thing as that makes suncream!"

said the , "I can feel it working already."

"And I never knew there was such a thing as a

white — and pink — !" laughed !

"Excellent work, Octonauts," said .

53

SPECIAL FEATURES: A whitetip shark can be very aggressive. It is able to sniff out its prey even if it is a long way away by lifting up its snout.

HABITAT: The Western Atlantic around the coast of America and the Hawaiian islands.

DIET: Bony fish such as tuna but also larger dead animals like whales.

CHALLENGE: Find a sticker of a pilot fish for this whitetip shark.

OCTOFACT:

A whitetip shark often has a pilot fish which follows it around and helps keep the shark clean. The shark never eats the pilot fish even when the little fish cleans the shark's teeth!

GUP-E IN ACTION!

Peso uses the GUP-E as his underwater ambulance.
If ever there is a creature in trouble he'll be there to help.

OCTOFACT:

This Gup is quick and easy to move around. It is perfect for exploring and research.

Find stickers of Peso and a shark to add to the scene.

THE BIG FACTS MEGA QUIZ

Is your head full of fishy facts? Are you the ultimate Octonauts fan? Test your knowledge here. There is only one correct answer for each question. Check your answers on page 59, then give yourself a reward sticker for every question you get right.

 WHITETIP SHARKS ARE FOLLOWED BY:

a) Clams

b) A star fish

c) A pilot fish

 FLYING FISH EAT:

a) Plankton

b) Seaweed

c) Flies

 CAPTAIN BARNACLES CAN OFTEN BE HEARD SAYING:

a) Octonauts, swim faster!

b) Octonauts, let's do this!

c) Octonauts, it's time for a rest!

4 THE ELECTRIC TORPEDO RAY CAN GIVE OFF:

a) A strong smell

b) A loud screech

c) An electric shock wave

5 WHICH GUP IS BEST FOR TOWING:

a) GUP-C

b) GUP-E

c) GUP-A

GUP-C   GUP-E   GUP-A

6 SHELLINGTON LOVES TO EAT:

a) Chocolate ice cream

b) Clam ice cream

c) Octopus ice cream

7 KWAZII'S GUP OF CHOICE IS THE:

a) GUP-A

b) GUP-B

c) GUP-D

8 PESO CAN BE HEARD SAYING:

a) Flappity flippers!

b) Flippity fish!

c) Flip, flap and away!

Answers on page 59.

ANSWERS

PAGES 26-27 KWAZII AND GUP-B

GUP-B appears 5 times.

The creatures are: sea urchin, carrier crab, octopus, seahorse.

PAGE 30 WATERY WORDS

Wave, fish, shell and sea.

PAGE 31 GUP RESCUE

Path B leads to GUP-E.

PAGE 32 DANGER ALERT!

The giant clam and cuttlefish are harmless. Whirlpools, jellyfish, electric torpedo rays and underwater volcanos can be dangerous.

PAGE 34 MIDNIGHT SHADOWS

A-2, B-3, C-1.

PAGES 36-37 LAB SPOTTING

 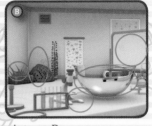

There are 3 test tubes in picture B.

PAGES 42-43 SHIVER ME WHISKERS

A pirate would own the chest, the map and the spyglass.

A-Tweak, B-Dashi, C-Inkling.

PAGES 44-45 SUBS IN ACTION!

PAGES 46-47 FREEZING FUN!

PAGES 56-57 THE BIG FACTS MEGA QUIZ

1-c, 2-a, 3-b, 4-c, 5-a, 6-b, 7-b, 8-a.

VEHICLE
ASSORTMENT

SHOOTS
WATER

OCTOPOD
PLAYSET

SOUND
THE
OCTO-ALERT!

OVER 10
PLAY
PIECES!

OCTONAUTS™

JOIN THE CREW!

MOVES THROUGH THE WATER

GUP-A MISSION VEHICLE

CTION FIGURE ASSORTMENT

CHARACTER ASSORTMENT

COLOUR CHANGE CREATURES

EXPLORE . RESCUE . PROTECT